A

Shapes for Lunch

by Deborah Schecter

ISBN: 978-0-545-25691-9

Illustrated by Anne Kennedy
Designed by Maria Lilja • Colored by Ka-Yeon Kim-Li
Copyright © 2010 by Deborah Schecter

All rights reserved. Published by Scholastic Inc. Printed in China.
10 9 8 7 6 5 4 3 2 1   68   21 22 23 24 25 26/0

SCHOLASTIC

I like to eat a square.

I like to eat a triangle.

I like to eat an oval.

I like to eat a rectangle.

I like to eat a circle.

I like to eat a half-circle.

Shapes are fun for lunch!